Ae

The Life and Loves of
Elsie Tanner

The Life and Loves of
Elsie Tanner

DARAN LITTLE

BOXTREE

Published in association with

GRANADA TELEVISION

ACKNOWLEDGEMENTS

The publishers would like to thank the following for their help in organising all the pictures for this book:

Kathryn de Belle, Alan Smyllie, Jim Rowan, David Collins, Tom Purslow and Ian Cartwright.

This book is dedicated to Mark Wells and all other Elsie fans.

First published in 1992 by Boxtree Limited

Coronation Street © Granada Television
Photographs © Granada Television

10 9 8 7 6 5 4 3 2 1

Editing and additional writing: Mary Lambert
Design: Penny Mills
Jacket design: Paterson-Jones
Printed and bound in Italy through OFSA

BOXTREE LIMITED
36 Tavistock Street
London WC2E 7PB

A CIP catalogue entry for this book is available from the British Library

ISBN 1 85283 177 4

Contents

Introduction

'I used to stand in the middle of our back yard and say to meself, "Elsie kid, one day you'll be someone."'

Elsie Tanner

Elsie Tanner, née Grimshaw, was born on the wrong side of town in a derelict slum, that had been long overdue for demolition. She moved into Coronation Street just after the start of World War 2 in November 1939. She was only sixteen at the time, but was already married, pregnant and unsure of her true feelings for her 28 year-old husband, Arnold. She had hardly settled in at Number 11 when Arnold was called up and went off to fight abroad. She was left to get to know the people in the street where she was to live, with a few short breaks, for most of her life.

From a young age Elsie was a natural fighter, she had learnt early on how to battle for food, warmth and affection as the eldest child in a large family of ten. If she saw something that she wanted she would do everything in her power to get it; this same attitude followed on in later life with her work and the many men she met in her turbulent love life.

By the time she was nineteen, Elsie was a mother of two children, Linda and Dennis. She often admitted she wasn't a good mother, but no matter how much she argued with or criticised her children, she loved them passionately, and always staunchly defended them when they were in trouble. When her husband returned home from the War and told her he wanted to leave her, Elsie was not unduly concerned as he had already given her the most treasured people in her life - her children.

She was a bold, glamorous, but uncompromising woman, who enjoyed living life to the full, and was often heard to comment: 'I'm a dirty great optimist - I keep looking for that rainbow round the corner'. She was extremely attractive to men and was not afraid to use her blatant sexuality to get the man she wanted. But despite getting married three times and

having many lovers, she never found that man who could suffer all her faults and just accept and love her, as she was, for life. She once sadly said: 'All I wanted, all I ever wanted, was to be loved...I just wanted somebody to look after me...to protect me'.

Once asked by her daughter why she always thought something better would happen tomorrow, Elsie was heard to reply: 'Eee kid, what other choice 'ave I got?'

Her Lovers

'Elsie Tanner's a loud-mouthed, pig-'eaded, painted tramp, wi' a bust-ful o' brassiere an' nowt on top. An' with the right man on 'er arm, she'd turn into the best wife a lad could wish for.'

Ena Sharples to Elsie Tanner

Men were Elsie Tanner's downfall, they were always attracted to her bold, glamorous sexuality, which she wore like a battle flag, and her easy, friendly manner with them. But even when she got them to the altar, she still didn't find true, everlasting love. On the failure of her third and final marriage she commented wistfully: 'Marriage to me meant prawn cocktails, white fur coats, snazzy cars and sweet nothings. When they all went down the drain, the rest of it went with them'. She was the first to admit that her whole aim in life was to find someone who truly loved her for herself and who was not going to try and use her. Tragically for Elsie she never found that faithful, caring man, but even with all the upsets she endured she had more fun and lovers in just a few years than most people ever have in a lifetime.

The most important men to feature in Elsie's life were her three husbands – Arnold, Steve and Alan, her best friend Len, and the man who kept proposing until she accepted, but sadly never married – Bill.

Arnold Tanner, Elsie's first seafaring husband, had deserted the family home way back in 1945 and when we first meet Elsie she is on her own again. When he came skulking back to see her in 1961, the children did not know or recognise him, as he had not kept in touch with them. The only reason Arnold had come back was that he wanted a divorce to marry his shopkeeper girlfriend, Norah. Elsie refused and warned Norah that 'orrible Arnold was just after her money. However, the tables were turned when Elsie was faced with the prospect of Arnold suing her for divorce over her wartime romances. She wanted her past kept out of the courts, so finally admitted defeat and agreed to divorce him.

Arnold Tanner

Elsie was hardly overjoyed when Arnold returned home after a 15 year absence in January 1961 (top). His request for a divorce (middle) was echoed by the new woman in his life, Norah Dawson (bottom)

Elsie's initial attraction to Arthur Dewhurst soon faded as he started to try to dominate and control her life

Elsie did not completely trust Walter Fletcher and insisted her best friend, Dot, gave her support on their first date

Whilst the divorce was proceeding in May 1961, Elsie started going out with Det. Sgt. Arthur Dewhurst. Their first meeting was unconventional to say the least. Her son Dennis found Arthur bleeding in the backyard after he had been beaten up, and when he came to and found Elsie staring down at him he declared gallantly that, 'he was seeing an angel'. Arthur was a homely soul and Elsie contemplated marrying him to provide a stable home for Dennis, who although 18 was often in trouble with the law. The romance was doomed to early failure as Arthur could not come to terms with Elsie's relaxed and easy way with other men. Eventually his overbearing possessiveness forced her to end the relationship.

Never long without a man, Elsie enjoyed a brief flirtation with Walter Fletcher, a local representative in June that year. On their first date she primly took along her best friend and workmate, Dot Greenhalgh for support.

Celebrating with Dot at the Hewitt's wedding in October of the same year, she was introduced to one of her enduring loves, Bill Gregory. Dot was initially attracted to the dashing Chief Petty officer, who looked so smart in his naval uniform, and made a play for him but he only had eyes for Elsie.

For their first date Bill managed to borrow a car, but they hadn't got far when it broke down. Crowded together into a phone box to call for help, Bill couldn't resist the close proximity to steal his first kiss and to tell Elsie how much he wanted her. Their whirlwind romance caused the more 'stable' women in the Street to comment jealously on Elsie's blatant lack of morals. Discovering the affair was putting her divorce in jeopardy, Elsie reluctantly stopped seeing Bill in the November for six months. During that time on her own again, she again created gossip by housekeeping for her best mate Len Fairclough when his wife left him in the April of the following year. Her closer attachment to Len soon faded when Bill came back into her life just a few months later.

Bill Gregory

Elsie put her divorce in jeopardy when she started to go out with Bill Gregory in October 1961

Elsie desperately wanted to marry Bill, but she then discovered he was already married

Phyllis Gregory came to visit her husband in Coronation Street knowing nothing of his passionate affair

Ena Sharples, the Street's gossip, ever wanting to interfere in people's lives, found out that Bill was married and broke the devestating news to Elsie: 'I know what you all think o'me. I just want you to know what's what before 'e 'urts you more than 'e has done. I won't see anyone on this Street made a fool of'. Elsie couldn't believe that Bill would deceive her but eventually he admitted he had a wife he couldn't bring himself to leave. When Phyllis Gregory arrived a month later, oblivious of her husband's affair, Bill reluctantly went home with her leaving Elsie heartbroken.

12

ookie Dave Smith entered Elsie's life for the first time in September 1962. She had placed a bet on a horse in the St Leger through her friend, Dot, and it had won. When Dave popped round with her meagre winnings, he took a fancy to her and offered her a night out with him instead. Laughingly he joked with her, 'Tangle with me an' you'll get nothing but trouble, but I'll promise you one thing – you'll enjoy it'. She happily agreed to the outing but their pre-meal drink at the Rovers was spoilt as Len was lurking jealously in a corner, watching their every move. Infuriated, Dave warned him off, but Len hit out and knocked him to the ground. Len was later charged with assault and bound over for a year. Elsie was furious with Len for his interference and determined to hurt him further went on holiday with the bookie.

Dave Smith

Dave Smith's first date with Elsie in late 1962 (top) was ruined by Len's jealousy (bottom)

Len Fairclough

Elsie and Len first met at school, but their enduring friendship was never really marriage material

As they got on so well it was inevitable that Elsie and Len would eventually get together. Their first date was in the following May at a dance held by the local builders at the Orinoco Club. But Elsie soon put a damper on Len's increasing ardour when she refused to have a serious relationship with him as he was still legally married. No one believed her, however, when she returned from holidaying alone in Blackpool the next month only to discover that, unknown to her, Len too had been staying at the resort at the same time.

Len's divorce was finalised in the November and he proposed to Elsie shortly afterwards. Ena and Dennis both wanted her to accept Len as they thought he would make a good husband, but she turned him down, saying: 'You're going to hate me for this. You'll think I'm a fool – we get on together, we fit, we belong but there's more to it than that. I get on wi' lots of men but I don't marry 'em'.

Only a month later, she upset Len even more by falling in love with Dennis's boss, Laurie Frazer, owner of the Orinoco Club where she and Len had their first date. Laurie showered Elsie with gifts and offered Elsie a job at his new sporting club. She accepted a position when he also employed Dennis.

Laurie Frazer

Len was bitterly upset (top) when Elsie started to go out with Laurie Frazer in December 1963. He was Dennis' boss at the Orinoco Club (left)

Mrs Frazer tried to humiliate Elise by telling her she was just one of Laurie's many women (right). In her fury, Elsie threw Laurie out of Number 11 and he and his wife left the area (bottom)

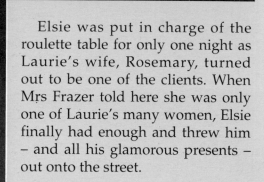

Elsie was put in charge of the roulette table for only one night as Laurie's wife, Rosemary, turned out to be one of the clients. When Mrs Frazer told here she was only one of Laurie's many women, Elsie finally had enough and threw him – and all his glamorous presents – out onto the street.

Needing to earn some extra money, Elsie started modelling at a local art school. The young teacher, David Graham, started becoming obsessed with Elsie and finally asked her to go out with him. Elsie was flattered by all the attention,

David Graham

Elsie enjoyed modelling in the evenings at the art school, but her teacher's obsession with her got out of hand

especially as David was the same age as Dennis, and agreed to the occasional meal out with him. However, it was not too long before she found out that David was mentally disturbed and when she tried to stop seeing him, he threatened to kill her. When he drew a gun, she was terrified but her tears brought him to his senses and he left her crying to be comforted by Dennis.

Dennis Tanner acted as the helpful chaperone during his mother's trial marriage to Len in December 1964

Elsie's enduring friend, Len Fairclough, still felt they would make the ideal married couple, and worn down by his persistence, Elsie suggested they should have a trial marriage in late 1964. Len soon grew frustrated when she refused to let him go to bed with her and after suffering for a week he agreed she was right.

Norman Lindley

Norman was smitten with Elsie and offered her the chance of a new life in Canada (left), but she was forced to stand down in favour of his wife, Florrie, who wanted him back (below)

The New Year brought another torrid romance when engineer Norman Lindley returned home after working for six years in the Far East. Whilst attempting a reconciliation with his wife he took out Elsie and soon begged her to join him to start a new life with him in Canada. She agreed to leave with him but was left desolated when his estranged wife, Florrie, decided to have him back after all.

Disillusionment with all men was making Elsie very bitter and some months later she decided to forget about a loving relationship and to just have a good time with a wealthy admirer. Deciding she needed to take some positive action, she waited in a Cheshire pub called the Fox and Hounds until she caught the eye of wealthy solicitor Bob Maxwell.

Bob Maxwell

When Bob crashed his car and died at the wheel, Elsie fled the scene in horror leaving behind her gloves in her haste

They soon got talking and at the end of the evening he offered to drive her home in his jaguar. When he stopped the car in a lay-by, Elsie's hopes of a passionate interlude were ruined when he just used the opportunity to tell her how his wife ill-treated him. The evening came to a shattering end when shortly after starting the car again he suffered a major heart attack, crashed the car and died at the wheel.

Distraught, Elsie fled the scene but was tracked down and forced to appear at the inquest where the devestated widow, Mrs Maxwell, called her a prostitute. Seeking support from her loyal friend, Len, Elsie had a furious row with him after he discovered they'd been in the lay-by for three hours. At his lowest ebb, Len screamed at her: 'You call me a louse, what the hell do you think you are – you're just nothing...you feel nothing, you're just paint and mush Elsie Tanner'.

As the years went on conditions and facilities in the Street improved all the time and at the beginning of 1966 Elsie decided to have a telephone installed. Jim Mount was the young, single GPO engineer who called to install the telephone at Number 11. Immediately attracted, Elsie flung herself into an affair with him but it soon cooled when he refused to marry her. He badly injured her pride when he left the Street to go off with Brenda Riley a barmaid who worked at the Rovers Return.

Jim Mount only came to install a telephone, but he and Elsie made a good connection! (top)

Percy Bridge convinced Elsie he was a courageous hero, but she was soon disillusioned (middle)

Dave Smith came to tell Elsie he'd rescued her grandson, producing Paul's cap as proof (bottom right)

Elsie was delighted when her daughter and son-in-law returned from Canada in the autumn, but her initial happiness was spoilt when her young grandson, Paul, was narrowly saved from drowning. As the family were recovering from the shock Percy Bridge appeared on the scene and announced that was the man who had rescued the young lad. Elsie, was very grateful to Percy and her warm feelings soon deepened into a relationship with him. She was disgusted at her own vulnerability to men when Dave Smith exposed Percy as a fraud who was just posing as her grandson's rescuer; Dave himself was in fact the true hero. Elsie was very grateful to Dave and their romance was rekindled, much to everyone's interest in the Street.

The US Army returned to barracks in nearby Burtonwood in the spring of 1967 after being away since the end of World War 2. Dot Greenhalgh, was delighted to be reunited with her old flame Gregg Flint but Elsie was reluctant to meet her old love Steve Tanner, feeling that too many years had passed since their last encounter. They had first fallen in love when she was still married to Arnold Tanner and she had been tempted to leave for a better life in America with him, but in the end her marriage and loyalty to her children had won.

Dot and Gregg conspired to bring the two old lovers together again. Elsie was thrilled to see that Steve had not changed at all and he swore that she still looked as stunning as the young 20 year-old he'd left behind.

Steve Tanner

Returning to Number 11 Coronation Street 20 years later in May 1967, Steve Tanner found his wartime sweetheart, Elsie, as young as ever and virtually unchanged

Steve proposed marriage to Elsie at the Roebuck Inn in Cheshire in August 1967. They had first met there all those years ago in 1943

Dave Smith wasn't so pleased that Steve had come back into Elsie's life and tried to show him that he wasn't welcome in the Street, but Elsie snubbed him and her friend Len to spend as much time as she could with Steve. When Steve was mugged one night and his cigarette case was stolen, Dave and Len immediately became the prime suspects. Dennis managed to get hold of the cigarette case and returned it to Steve who immediately thought he'd received it from Len. Steve and Gregg decided to teach Len a lesson he wouldn't forget and beat him up. The mystery was solved when Walter Greenhalgh confessed to Elsie that he had attacked Steve mistaking him for Gregg whom his wife Dot was having an affair with.

The attraction and love Elsie and Steve had felt before was soon stronger than ever, and it was only a few months before Steve proposed to Elsie at the Roebuck Inn and she happily accepted. Marriage was to take Elsie away from the Street as Steve rented a luxury flat for them both in prosperous Altrincham in Cheshire.

Elsie couldn't resist inviting all her girl friends for a riotous all-day hen party at Tatton Park in Knutsford. Her marriage took place at St Stephen's Methodist Church on September 4th 1967. Dennis gave his mother away and Dot Greenhalgh and Linda Cheveski were Elsie's Matrons of Honour.

Marriage September 4th 1967

A coach was hired to carry all the residents of Coronation Street to Warrington for Elsie's marriage to Steve Tanner (top). Linda was maid of honour and Gregg Flint was best man (left)

The couple went off to honeymoon in Lisbon in Portugal before returning to their new home in Altrincham. Elsie soon became restless and bored, living miles away from the Street, where all her old friends lived. Her posh neighbours never really tried to get to know her, but she made a close friend in her cleaning lady, May.

Fed up with being at home, she announced that she wanted to go back to work but Steve stopped her saying he much preferred having her at home to look after the flat. She had no sooner resigned herself to that fact when Steve announced he was being posted back to America. Deep depression settled on Elsie at the thought of leaving all her family and friends so far behind. Len begged her to stay asking her to leave Steve and return to the Street, but in the end Elsie decided her place must be with her husband and after a happy family Christmas at Number 11, the Tanners emigrated.

The happy glow of their honeymoon in Portugal was shortlived (opposite) *when Steve had to go back to America. Len begged Elsie to leave Steve* (top) *but she wanted to make her marriage work and left with him in late 1967* (bottom)

Elsie Tanner returned home in March 1968 a sad and dispirited woman. Her short time in America had seen the death of her marriage and her self respect. Her old pal, Len Fairclough, was the only one to truly understand what she was going through and to give her the help she needed

Living in America was hard for Elsie to get used to, Steve made no effort to introduce her to her new lifestyle or integrate her with his wealthy friends, leaving her alone more and more. After three months she was forced to take stock, her fairytale romance was falling apart. Steve admitted he no longer loved her and asked for a posting to Panama. Realising the marriage was over Elsie bitterly said: 'Five minutes back in America an' 'e was part of it all like 'e'd never been gone. It was like a wall came down. An' I was left on the outside, lookin' in. An' you find out you're just two strangers. It's not the dramatic Sunday newspaper stuff. All the things they did I didn't know about – the golfing, the bridging, the sailing. I could 'ave learned but Steve was impatient. He wouldn't wait for me to catch up. It was ridiculous, two middle-aged people, and' we couldn't even live together like...well, perhaps lovers was too much to ask, I'd o' settled for friends. He said leaving me twenty years ago was 'is first big mistake – coming back to me was 'is second.'

Broke and feeling very alone Elsie had to sell her engagement ring to pay for her flight home. Whilst her neighbours speculated about her sudden return, Elsie gave up caring what she looked like and sank into a deep depression. It was Len who came round regularly to cheer her up. By boosting her morale he gradually gave her back her shattered dignity and told her to forget Steve and that she was by far the better person.

Steve often sent money to Elsie from abroad, but she refused to touch it, and putting a brave face on she took a job at Dave Smith's florist shop and soon slipped back to her old flirtatious ways with him.

Dot Greenhalgh was delighted to see her old flame Gregg Flint when he came back in September 1968 (left). *But the news of Steve's brutal death* (middle) *brought about a public inquest. Len was the police's prime suspect* (bottom) *and he was forced to take part in an identity parade*

Some months later Gregg Flint, Steve's Tanner old buddy returned to Weatherfield as their unit was again stationed in Burtonwood. Steve was back with them and he sent Gregg to tell Elsie that he wanted her back. When they met again Elsie at first refused to listen to Steve's pleadings, but gradually weakening, she tried to convince him their marriage was over, but deep in her heart, she did not trust herself not to return to Steve.

A new life with Steve was not to be as he was found brutally murdered at the bottom of the stairs in his flat in September 1968. Both Elsie and Len were suspects and were called to give evidence at the subsequent inquest. Owing to lack of evidence the coroner's verdict was given as accidental death.

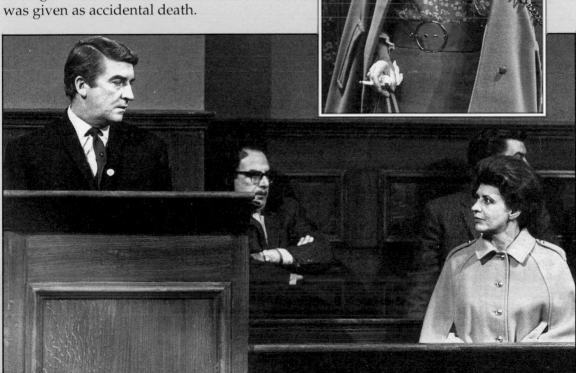

Lilian Smith decided to use her husband's continuing affair with Elsie as grounds for her divorce petition in 1969

After a few months of grieving as a widow and tired of being on her own again, Elsie put her heart into her affair with Dave Smith. Their closeness alienated Elsie even from Len who declared that he didn't trust Dave. His feelings were nearly proved right when Dave's estranged wife Lilian appeared back in his life to tell him she was divorcing him and naming Elsie as correspondent. Fed up with being caught in the middle, Elsie finished with Dave declaring in disgust, 'Just once, for a change, I'd like to get pally with a feller whose idea of a good time isn't landing me in muck'.

It certainly wasn't love at first sight when Elsie first met a wealthy newcomer to the Street, Alan Howard. He arrived from Leeds in December 1969 and annoyed her with his condescending and patronising manner to her neighbours and the locals. She softened towards him when he asked her to become the manageress of his hair salon. It wasn't long before they were going out together and Elsie was won over by his wit and charm and the money he lavished on her.

Just when the relationship was going well, Bill Gregory, newly widowed, appeared back on the scene in February 1970 and asked Elsie to marry him. He was buying a wine bar in Portugal with a Navy friend and wanted Elsie to go out there with him. But when Alan begged her to stay with him, Elsie realised she was in love with him and allowed Bill to leave her life once again.

To keep up his extravagant lifestyle, Alan bought a big country house and told Elsie she could think of it as hers. Elsie was thrilled but was also scared of the thought of any

Newcomer Alan Howard initially upset people with his patronising attitude (top). *Len did not want to get involved when Bill Gregory came back on the scene at the height of Elsie's affair with Alan* (left)

firm commitment. When she felt more settled in the relationship and started talking about marriage, Alan suddenly deserted her and returned to Leeds.

Feeling rejected and all alone again, Elsie couldn't be bothered to go anywhere and her appearance deteriorated Alan, returning from Leeds a couple of months later, was shocked by her unkempt state, and realising he did love her proposed to her so they can be together always. Elsie still felt very hurt and refused to believe he meant what he said and asked Len to get rid of him for her. Alan persisted in winning back her affections and eventually Elsie accepted him.

Marriage July 22nd 1970

Alan Patrick Howard married Elsie with Len as his best man (top). Their initial attraction had developed in to a strong and passionate love

Elsie Tanner became a wife for the third time when she became Mrs Alan Howard on July 22nd 1970 in a registry office ceremony with Len and Bet Lynch as the official witnesses. After a romantic honeymoon in Paris, Elsie was stunned to learn on their return that Alan was virtually insolvent. He owned a garage locally and two hair salons in Leeds and they had always seemed so profitable, but he had not run the businesses well and had run up several debts.

Alan was declared legally bankrupt and Elsie found it hard to deal with his broken pride as well as a new marriage. Slowly the Howard's paid off his crippling debts and actually became closer as they fought to become solvent again. Alan supported Elsie when she heard the bad news that American army deserter, Joe Donnelli, back lodging in the Street, had finally confessed to killing Steve Tanner about an unpaid debt, before committing suicide himself.

Alan kept the news of his business insolvency from Elsie until after they were married (top)

Dennis Maxwell tried to tempt Elsie into an affair, but she refused (left)

Marriage was good for the Howard's until Dennis Maxwell, started to take an interest in Elsie in the spring of the next year. He was her boss at the Warehouse where she worked as a supervisor in the checking department. He made no effort to hide the fact that he found Elsie very attractive. She was flattered by his attentions, but assured Alan that she wasn't interested. Overcome by jealousy he could not bring himself to believe her.

33

As their marriage started to break down, rows became a daily occurrence in the Howard household

Alan was so convinced that Elsie had betrayed him that to get his own back he secretly started to take out Janet Reid, who worked at the local corner shop. It wasn't long before Elsie found out and confronted Janet and told her angrily to leave her husband alone, declaring: 'I know your sort – off with the old and on with the new'.

Dennis Maxwell was very impressed with Elsie's work at the warehouse and offered her promotion in September 1971 to the Birmingham division where he had moved to. Elsie would have liked the job and the increased salary that went with it, but turned it down because he was a dishonest manager. Alan seemed disinterested when she told him her decision and hurt her badly by telling her he didn't care what she did any more. He left saying he needed some time alone and slept rough in his garage for a couple of weeks. Elsie was left to celebrate alone over Christmas.

While he was away, Alan borrowed some money from his ex-wife Laura to buy another garage business. When he came home to Elsie he refused to tell her where it had come from. Elsie finally discovered about the money from Laura herself and then annoyed Alan by refusing to let Laura give them the loan as a gift.

Alan's ex-wife, Laura, was willing to write off the loan she gave to them, but Elsie's pride would not let her

Jimmy Frazer, was an overpowering second-hand car salesman who entered Elsie and Alan's lives when he went into partnership with Alan and started to sell cars outside his garage. He annoyed Elsie with his arrogant attitude and she was upset when he started to become very friendly with Alan. Matters went from bad to worse when Jimmy used Alan as his frontman in a night club venture. To Elsie's fury, Alan then began to spend all his evenings down at the Capricorn Club flirting with nightclub hostess Rita Littlewood. When Rita started to get seriously interested in Alan, Elsie confronted her and told her to leave him alone.

Life degenerated further for the Howard's when Alan started drinking too much at the club. He was becoming a virtual alcoholic and was only forced into slowing down when Elsie threatened to leave him. Worn down by all the upsets they had endured Alan and Elsie jumped at the chance of moving and starting afresh when Elsie was offered another promotion in late 1973, but this time in Newcastle.

Alan's involvement with Jimmy Frazer (top) led to his subsequent friendship with Rita Littlewood, much to Elsie's annoyance (left)

A new job working for Brittain's warehouse in Alan's native Newcastle was offered to Elsie in late 1973

35

In Elsie's absence Len had fallen for Rita Littlewood (top). She ruined Elsie's budding romance with Ted Brownlow (right) when she let it slip that Elsie had been married three times

The patchy married life of Alan and Elsie did not improve as hoped in Newcastle and three years later, finally admitting it was all over, Elsie returned to Weatherfield without her husband. In her absence, Len had grown close to Rita Littlewood and they were married in April 1977. Elsie was initially too upset at the news to attend the ceremony, but managed to put a brave face on it and went to the reception.

She hadn't been there long before Ted Brownlow, the hotel manager hosting the occasion, noticed that she was alone and made it clear that he found her attractive and would like to see her again. To Elsie's surprise, several romantic meals followed with Ted treating her with champagne and tempting delicacies from the hotel kitchens. Before the relationship could get interesting Ted discovered from Rita that Elsie had already been married three times and soon stopped the relationship.

ife on her own had never appealed to Elsie and after a few months she went to Newcastle to see Alan, hoping for a reconciliation. But she was to be bitterly disappointed, rather than agreeing to get together again he told her that he wanted a divorce to marry his younger secretary. Upset and disillusioned with marriage she returned home and was further distressed when the post on her birthday brought with it her divorce papers. She decided to cheer herself by dressing up and going out on the town. But even this took a turn for the worse, when she was mistaken for a prostitute by a businessman.

Elsie enjoyed being treated to champagne, first of all by Bernard Lane who unfortunately mistook her for a prostitute (top), and then by tycoon, Harry Payne, on her holiday in sunny Majorca (bottom)

The failure of her last marriage hit Elsie hard and it took a long time to regain her self respect and after a while she sought solace with her daughter in Birmingham. Changing her name back to Tanner also made her feel that she was independent once again.

Taxi driver, Ron Mather, entered her life at this time and she was pleased when he didn't try and rush her into a serious relationship. Gradually they saw more of each other and after he was roughly beaten up in his taxi she insisted he stayed the night for the first time. The following month they decided to go off on holiday together to Majorca. Elsie enjoyed herself abroad by flirting with tax exile, Harry Payne who befriended the couple on their arrival on the island. Ron did not enjoy the happy threesome as much as Elsie did and was very put out when Harry turned up at Number 11 shortly after their arrival home. Elsie enjoyed the drama of two men fighting over her, but Ron told Harry he wasn't welcome, in no uncertain terms, and sent him packing.

Late in 1979 Ron took a chauffeur's job in Torquay and persuaded Elsie to sell up Number 11, which she'd eventually bought, and go with him as housekeeper. The venture soon backfired when the boss started paying attention to Elsie and Ron refused to protect her. Elsie had had enough and left Ron and Torquay behind and returned home.

Elsie gave up both her job and her precious home to work in Torquay with Ron Mather in late 1979

Working at Jim's café the following summer, Elsie took a liking to Lorry driver Dan Johnson who talked her into giving him bed and breakfast. Never learning her lesson with men he soon became a lover. Dan wasn't that interested and to Elsie's fury started seeing barmaid Bet Lynch. Elsie in her despair lamented: 'What pride have I got left? I've tottered around on five-inch heels up an' down this street for the last 20. An' for what? To catch meslef a feller. And everybody's known it'.

Furious that she could be so susceptible to men, Elsie threw him and his belongings out into the street. Her next

Dan Johnson's roving eye couldn't keep him with Elsie for long, and he was soon attracted to Bet Lynch at the Rovers, which caused a fight with Elsie

lodger Wally Randle was a quiet man who was very polite, friendly and considerate to Elsie. After giving him his key to Number 11, Elsie made it clear that she would like to be more than his landlady. Wally's response was one of horror and throwing chivalry to the wind he returned the key, telling her she was too old for him. This key had gone back and forth so many times that Ena Sharples once commented: 'There must be more latchkeys for Number 11 Coronation Street, than there is for Buckin'am Palace'.

Elsie first met her new lodger, Wally Randle, at Jim's café where he stopped two men fighting

At this time Elsie was getting more downhearted by the day, she hated her job in the café and was in desperate need of some friendly male company, so shortly after Wally moved out she picked up rough Bill Fielding in a pub and took him home for the night. In the cold light of morning they couldn't wait to get away from each other. On her way out she told him that she'd been drunk and wouldn't want to see him again but got the cutting reply: 'Oh, didn't you enjoy yourself or some'at...I think I must have been drunk as well seeing you in broad daylight'.

Bet played gooseberry when Elsie picked up Bill Fielding in a club in the spring of 1981

Dot Stockwell told Elsie what she thought of her in no uncertain terms for stealing her beloved, husband Wilf

Elsie was still trying to get over the humiliation of the incident when Bill's wife tracked her down and wrecked the house, slashing all Elsie's clothes.

Back working with Mike Baldwin at Baldwin's Casuals, this time as a humble machinist, in late 1981, Mike asked Elsie one day to help him land an important order by entertaining buyer, Wilf Stockwell. The entertaining went rather too well and Elsie made a big impression on Wilf who started taking her out. Unknown to Elsie, Wilf was desperate to get away from his wife and to Elsie's amazement he suddenly announced he was leaving his wife for her. Elsie was horrified at the prospect of breaking up a home, especially with someone she hardly knew, and tried to stop him.

Wilf left his wife for Elsie, but she was unsure about the affair and refused to commit herself

Before long Mrs Stockwell found out about the affair and where Elsie worked and came down to the factory to scream abuse at her, calling her nothing but a slut. In her fury she used her influence on Wilf's boss to get the order cancelled.

Elsie's workmates sent her to Coventry when the Stockwell affair lost the firm a big order

Elsie just wanted to get her life back to normal and persuaded Wilf that living with her wouldn't work and they went their separate ways.

Car salesman Geoff Siddall came into Elsie's life briefly in the autumn of 1982, he treated her well and offered to take her away on a holiday to Belgium. But Elsie and her suitcases waited in vain outside Number 11 for Geoff. He didn't turn up and she found out he'd absconded with his firms' wages. In December 1983 Elsie suffered one of the biggest blows of her life, Len Fairclough was killed in a car crash and Elsie wept bitterly for her best friend.

Bill Gregory returned from abroad and whisked Elsie off to start a new and better life in Portugal in January 1984

Not long after, Bill Gregory, who'd served with Len during World War 2, returned to give his condolences to Len's grieving widow, Rita, and was surprised to find that Elsie still lived in the Street. He started to take her out again and knowing that she was at her lowest ebb, he finally persuaded her to leave the Street behind once and for all and to go back with him and start a new life in the sun running his wine bar in the Algarve.

Family Ties

'I've kept that home together with sweat and blood. I've been wage-earner, cook and mother for my son for t'past 15 years.'

Elsie Tanner to Ena Sharples

However disasterous Elsie's early marriage to Arnold Tanner was, it did leave her with a family. Dennis and Linda despite having inherited all their parents many faults comforted, loved and cared for Elsie when she needed them and gave her something to live and fight for in her life. She was not a good mother in the conventional sense, and was basically scared of the responsibility of children, but she did love them dearly and in later life was happy to pass on her mistakes in raising them to other people.

Elsie's son, Dennis Tanner, was born on April 1st 1942, but insisted like the Queen, on celebrating his official birthday on April 10th every year. He was mainly brought up his elder sister, Linda, who used to take him out in the street to play when their mum was

Dennis

His sister, Linda Tanner, (below) was often the mainstay in Dennis' life (below right) as he grew up without the strong support of a father

entertaining one of her new fellers. Arnold Tanner deserted his children in 1945, and without a strong father image, Dennis ran circles round his mother and enjoyed playing truant from school for most of his school years.

He left school hardly able to read and write, but he had become very streetwise. Bored and restless he was led into a life of petty crime by Jed Stone, and one night both the lads were caught one night robbing a newsagents and were sent to Borstal for six months. He was released in 1960 and found it difficult to get a job because of his criminal record.

One night Dennis came home grinning from ear to ear with £25 in his pocket and refused to tell Elsie where he got it. When the police came round to interview him as a suspect about a local burglary, Elsie upset him by presuming he must had done it. A neighbour solved the mystery by saying that he had seen Dennis winning the money at the Dogs.

To Elsie's amazement, he turned his back on crime, and announced he was going into show business. Before long life was turned upside down at Number 11, Elsie had to contend with strippers arriving at all hours up to be interviewed by impresario Dennis. One, La Composita, had a pet python and Dennis agreed to keep it at home for her. When Elsie found it in a box she took a liking to it, much to Dennis' surprise. Another time Dennis was asked to babysit for a chimp called Rupert. Elsie only found out when she discovered him sitting in the kitchen sink. Horrified she shouted at her son: 'Dennis Tanner, I think it's time we had one o' our little chats. Why's there a gorilla sittin' in me sink!' Rupert then escaped from the house and caused havoc at the Rovers. Ena never lived it down when he was eventually found sitting in her chair in the snug – minus her glass of stout!

Shortly afterwards Dennis put on a show at the Mission. At the end of the evening he was left to look after two seal lions, Bonny and Cherry, for the night. As

Elsie took a definite liking to an eight-foot python that Dennis was looking after

Elsie gathered all her family around her for Christmas 1967

Jenny Sutton

Young Londoner, Jenny, started going out with Dennis in January 1968

Jack and Annie Walker were away for the night he borrowed their key from a neighbour and decided the animals would be happiest wallowing in their bath (the only one in the Street in 1962). He also let three chorus girls sleep in the Walker's bed. Unfortunately the Walker's arrived home early and Annie on walking in said coldly to her husband: 'Jack, there's some sea lions in our bath'. To which Jack replied: 'That's nothing love there's three young ladies in our bed!'

When Elsie was married to Steve Tanner and living in Altrincham in 1967 Dennis took in theatrical families. An acrobatic family called the Cooks moved in and Mrs Cook soon dominated Number 11 making poor Dennis feel like a lodger in his own home. When he took in a six-piece girls pipe band, Elsie stepped in and said enough was enough and got rid of them. Elsie was more than relieved when Dennis decided to change his career and try his hand at hairdressing.

When she got married to Steve Tanner, Elsie lent heavily on Dennis for emotional support and he told her was proud to give her away. It wasn't long afterwards that Dennis himself was to get married. He started going out with Jenny Sutton in early 1968 when her sister, Monica, was a member of a group of hippies who squatted at Number 11 with Dennis' approval. Elsie first met her when she was back at Number 11 after her unhappy stay in

America, and the couple had returned from a holiday in London. She didn't take to Jenny at first because she realised she was too much like a mirror image of herself.

Elsie prudishly banished Dennis to sleeping alone downstairs

Dennis and Jenny pretended to Elsie they had got married in London so they could share a bed together, but Elsie saw through their lie and, much to their amusement, she insisted that Dennis slept downstairs. This provoked him to berate her: 'By what right d'ya account yourself a guardian of public morals'. Jenny eventually won Elsie round by refusing to give Dennis up. After a short engagement, Dennis and Jenny married were married in a local registry office in May 1968. Dennis had last-minute nerves and woke up Elsie and

Elsie told Dennis the true facts about married life just before his wedding to Jenny in May 1968

Marriage May 29th 1968

The residents of the Street happily celebrated the Tanner wedding in style (top). Elsie was pleased to give Dennis her blessing when he took Jenny as his wife (right)

Linda in the early hours of his wedding day to talk through whether he was doing the right thing with them. Elsie hadn't touched a penny of Steve Tanner's alimony that he'd sent to her and gave it all, £250 worth, to Dennis as a wedding present. The couple did not want to live in the Street and moved away to start a new life in Bristol.

Marriage suited Dennis for a while, but he started to get bored in his job as a sales representative and Jenny began to irritate him – she was always nagging and wanted more money to spend on herself and on things for the house. Finally after five years their marriage broke up and Dennis was keen to make some easy money. He got involved with selling bogus double glazing to OAPs, but the scam was discovered by the police and he was sent to Pentonville jail in London for three years.

Elsie visited Dennis in Pentonville prison shortly after he was jailed. She blamed herself for what had happened, telling herself she had always been a bad, neglectful mother. In her distressed mood she walked around restlessly in a nearby park, leaving her handbag on a park bench. A speeding taxi knocked her unconscious and she was rushed to Guy's hospital. She was in a coma for a week and having no identification on her, no one could inform her husband of the time, Alan Howard. Alan thought Elsie was visiting a friend in Sheffield as she was too afraid to tell him that Dennis was in prison.

Elsie was knocked down by a reckless taxi driver and left unconscious on a London pavement

By the time Elsie came round in the hospital Alan had convinced himself that she had run off with another man, and he suspected it was her boss, Dennis Maxwell. When Alan was finally contacted by the hospital he rushed down to collect her. Sitting by her hospital bed he heard Elsie mumble, 'Dennis' and was furious thinking he had been right all along. It wasn't until Elsie was fully conscious again that she could explain the whole story.

Alan finally tracked Elsie down when she came round in Guy's hospital after a week in a coma

Linda Tanner, like her mother, had been attracted to the American GIs stationed locally and been engaged to one before she met Ivan Cheveski, who was Polish, at a friendship dance at the Town Hall. They were married a year later in 1958 and moved to Warrington to live. Ivan was very possessive and found it hard to accept Linda's flirtatious and friendly manner with other men. Depressed by feeling trapped in her marriage Linda returned home to Elsie for Christmas 1960, telling her the marriage was over. Elsie managed to get the couple together again when Linda found out that she was pregnant.

To please Linda, Ivan bought Number 9, next door to

Elsie, so that the Tanners could be reunited again. When baby Paul Cheveski was born in June 1961, Elsie couldn't accept that she was a grandmother at the tender age of 38. The Cheveski's decision to emigrate to Canada only a few months later brought out all Elsie's maternal feelings. At first, she refused to let her daughter leave but was reluctantly forced to acknowledge that Linda had her own life to lead. Sadly she said to her: 'I just don't understand you. I just don't understand you at all. What's the matter with you kids? One minute you're 'ere and the next minute you're gone'.

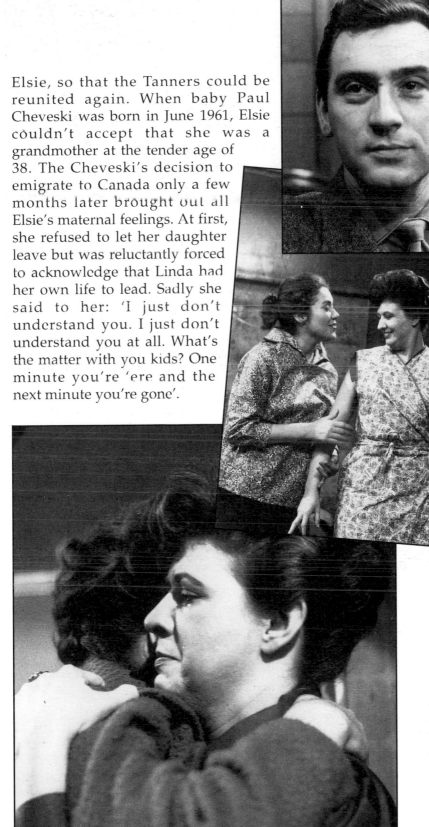

Linda and Ivan Cheveski

Ivan Cheveski (top) *bought Number 9 Coronation Street for £565 in May 1961 to keep the Tanner family together* (middle). *Seven months later the young married couple emigrated to Canada* (left)

Elsie comforted Linda as her son fought for his life after his accident (bottom). Later mother and daughter celebrated his complete recovery (bottom right)

Trouble brewed again in the Cheveski marriage again when Linda, bored in her marriage, found herself an Canadian boyfriend. Deciding she wanted to leave Ivan, Linda returned to Weatherfield in the autumn of 1966 for a break, bringing her two sons Paul and the new toddler, Martin. Elsie anxious to save the marriage, urged her to go and live with Ivan when he followed her and got a job in Birmingham. Linda refused and made plans to return to her Canadian boyfriend. This prompted an enraged response from Elsie: 'You're a thick headed little slut! I've got a conscience, madam, which is a damn sight more than you've got! I've given up things you'll never know about to put meself straight with you and our Dennis. You think all you've got to do is to get back to lover boy and the rest of your life's going to be evenings at the country club... You know nothing. I could have had what you think you're going to get three times a year over the last ten years.'

As there was stalemate with the Cheveski's, young Paul was sent to the local school in Bessie Street. The family was mortified when he disappeared on his way home from school in the autumn of 1966. Elsie had been late picking him up and never forgave herself. He had fallen in the canal but had been rescued by an unknown hero who had dragged

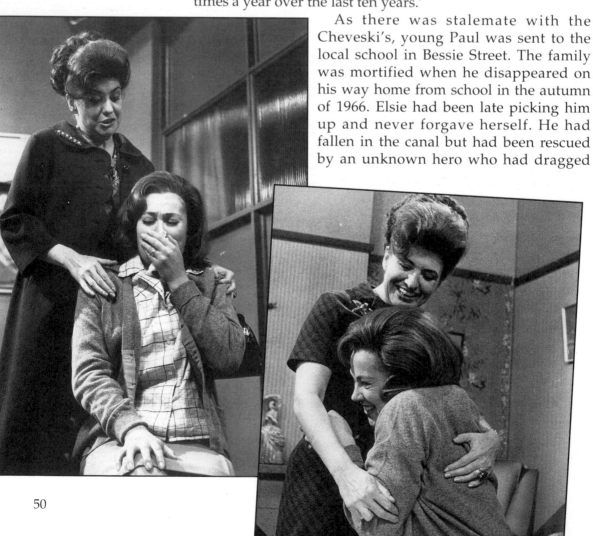

him from the water. Elsie comforted Linda who broke down when the child later developed pneumonia.

When Jerry Booth, Len Fairclough's business partner came round to offer his sympathies about the accident, he let it slip that Len, a local councillor, had voted against a fence being built next to the canal because it was too expensive. Elsie and Dennis were furious to hear the news and confronted Len who managed to appease them when he told his side of the story. He was not so lucky with Ivan. Reading about the Council's decision in the local paper he was devestated to think that they cared more about money than people's lives. He decided to make Len the scapegoat and going round to his builder's yard, he viciously attacked him with a plank of wood. Elsie and Linda heard the commotion and managed to separate the fighting pair.

Linda's plans to return to her new man in Canada were ruined when her boyfriend wrote to her saying that he'd found someone else, so reluctantly she stayed on in the Street. Young Paul's recovery reconciled the Cheveski's and together they left to start a new life in Birmingham. Their home became a welcome refuge for Elsie in times of trouble.

When Elsie left Coronation Street for good in 1984, she did so clutching precious photographs of her children, Dennis and Linda.

Ivan used Len as a scapegoat for Paul's accident and sought his revenge

Elsie left the Street in early 1984 clutching pictures of her family

The Lodgers

'Give me one good reason why I should let you come an' live 'ere. I'll give you one! I'm daft.'

Elsie Tanner to Gail Potter

Christine Appleby

Left all alone, the young widow, Christine Appleby, turned to Elsie for help and a roof over her head

Once both her children had grown up and left home, Elsie became lonely. She was a gregarious woman and loved having people around. She had never been content with her own company and soon yearned to have someone else living in Number 11. The idea of having a lodger appealed to her and going against the existing tenancy agreement with her landlord she rented a room to a local young widow, Christine Appleby.

Christine went to work with Elsie at Miami Modes in late 1962 and discovered that working and living with her was not as much fun as she thought it would be. Elsie interfered too much in Christine's life, and annoyed her by involving herself in her love affair with Frank Barlow. Desperate to get away from Number 11, but scared of having an open row with her, Christine sent an anonymous letter a few months later to Elsie's landlord, Wormold, telling him Elsie was violating her lease by sub-letting a room. Wormold

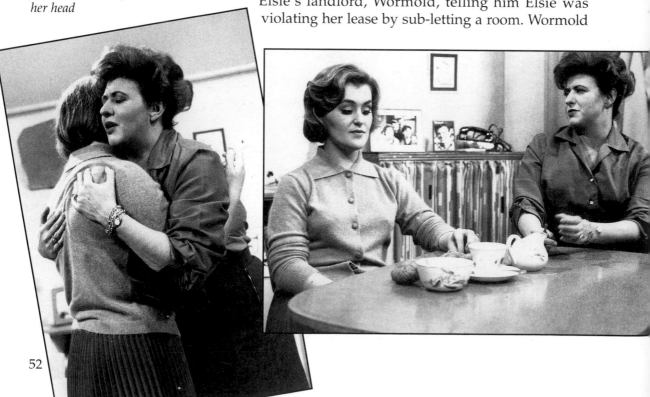

52

Elsie offended Len by accusing him of letting her landlord, Wormold, know that she had a secret lodger

got in touch with Elsie and insisted that Christine move out.

Elsie was furious that someone had informed on her and accused Len Fairclough of writing the letter before Christine confessed that she had done it. Elsie couldn't believe it and shouted at her, 'People think you're ever such a nice girl round 'ere Widow Appleby, but they want to follow you 'ome some time'. The fact that Christine admitted she wanted to live with Esther Hayes, an old street resident,

Esther Hayes supported Christine against Elsie over where she should live

Unaware of Elsie's upsets, Dennis innocently let the bailiffs in on his return from London in April 1963

Elsie fought the bailiffs in the Street to save her precious belongings

made Elsie feel even more humiliated and she had a blazing row with Esther.

Wormold was not to give up easily and demanded that Elsie paid some back rent for the period Christine was living in Number 11. Elsie refused to pay him and barricaded herself in the house. Her son Dennis returned home from London in the middle of the battle and unknowingly let the bailiffs in. As they removed her furniture and started putting it out in the street, Elsie cried out in despair: 'Just because somebody sticks up for herself and stands up for her rights...that table cost me four quid eight years ago at Jack Smedley's and I know that left leg's gone. But I don't care because I'm common!' Realising she would soon have no home Elsie finally gave in and paid the existing arrears.

Elsie didn't learn her lesson from the incident, and soon agreed to take in part-time singer and window cleaner Walter Potts and rented him Linda's old room. Dennis had originally smuggled him in during his show business days when Walter had been thrown out by his old landlady for singing and practising the guitar too loudly. Elsie

discovered Walter in her chair one
morning, but after hearing Dennis'
pleadings agreed to let him stay
saying: 'You can stay on one condition. That yer kids the
landlord as well as yer've kidded me. We're not supposed to
'ave lodgers round 'ere. So if anybody asks ya, you don't live
at the Tanners.'

Laurie Frazer, Dennis' boss took over Walter's career and
launched him in the pop world as singer Brett Falcon. He
was an overnight sensation and had a hit record called 'Not
too little, not too much'. In early 1964 he left to go on a
European tour, but was terrified to leave Number 11 because
of the hoards of screaming teenage girls outside. Elsie told
him to go out and make the most of the opportunity, saying,
'Why not swank if you've got a bit of somethin' worth
swankin' about. I remember the preenin' I did the day I
turned platinum blonde. I'm not kiddin', I couldn't so much
as pass a mirror!' Before he left Walter paid for the Tanners
to have a bath installed in his old room as he had been so
grateful for their help and encouragement.

Walter Potts

*Walter came into the
Tanner's lives as a
humble window cleaner
in the summer of 1963
and left a short time later
as a rising pop star*

T he summer of 1966 was a very overcrowded one in the
Tanner household. Elsie had both Dennis and Linda
staying with her, and had also taken in Sheila Birtles.
Sheila had lived nearby and got involved with a married man,
Neil Crossley. He had ended the affair when he'd discovered
she was pregnant. Sheila in despair had attempted suicide but
was saved by Dennis. She had left the Street to live with her

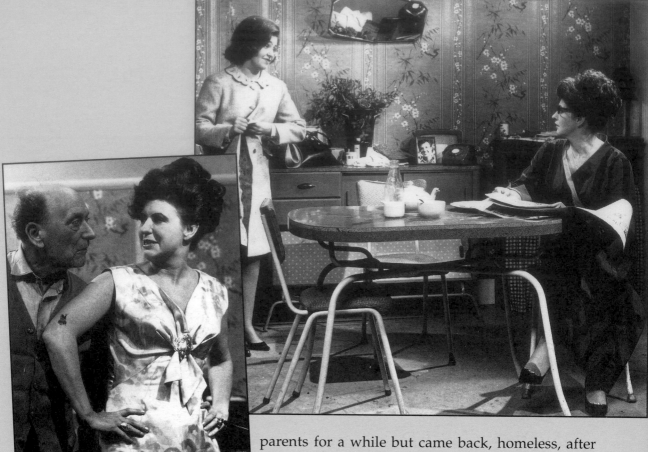

The summer of 1966 was a busy one in the Tanner household, apart from Dennis and Linda, Sheila Birtles (top right) came to stay, and Wally Tanner (top) turned up for a visit

parents for a while but came back, homeless, after she had fostered out her young son Danny. Elsie took her in out of pity and gave her Dennis' room.

Elsie's ex father-in-law, Wally Tanner turned up for a visit at the same time and took over the parlour. He was an unsavoury character. A former rag and bone man he'd degenerated into a tramp and a bit of a rogue. Elsie was annoyed by the old man overstaying his welcome and using her house for poker games with the local pensioners. He even had the nerve to try and court Minnie Caldwell from Number 5. Because the house was so full Linda was forced to share Elsie's bed, and Dennis had to sleep on the sofa. Dennis got fed up with the overcrowding and moaned to Elsie one morning: 'D'you remember when we used t'ave breakfast on us own. Just you 'an me, an' a quiet cough over 'ur tea an' fags. It were sort o' poetic in a way.'

Two months of having Wally in the house was quite enough for Elsie and she finally got rid of him by taking him down to her ex-husband Arnold's sweet shop and telling him in no uncertain terms that he was his responsibility: 'You'll find a good bed here. With your son. You can mek him paper aeroplanes and tek him for walks in t'park. You're a lovely couple. And it's nice to think it wer' me that brought you together again'.

Sheila meanwhile had taken up with her old plumber boyfriend, Jerry Booth. Their blossoming love affair was threatened by his pending divorce case, when Jerry's father-in-law hired a private detective to check up on the couple. For once Elsie joined forces with the nosy Ena Sharples and fed the detective completely false information at £2 a time, which she then gave to Sheila. Jerry later proposed to Sheila but she had met her old love, Neil again and they went off to start a new life with their child, Danny. Elsie was relieved to be without any lodgers for a while and to have the house to herself again.

Old enemies Elsie and Ena Sharples joined forces to mislead a private detective (inset) who was investigating Jerry Booth's personal life prior to his divorce

57

Gary Bailey, Elsie's nephew, turned out to be only a short-term lodger in the spring of 1968

Ray Langton

Ray became Elsie's lodger shortly after Gary left, but although initially pleased that people thought he was her lover (bottom), his later unwelcome attentions meant he didn't stay long (bottom right)

When Dennis got married in May 1968 his new wife Jenny and Linda feared Elsie would be lonely after Dennis had left for Bristol, and surprised her by persuading Gary Bailey, her nephew, to lodge with her. He only stayed a couple of weeks and Elsie rented his room to Ray Langton, who had just moved to the area and was working with Len Fairclough at his building yard. When people started presuming Ray was another of Elsie's lovers she felt flattered, but wasn't so pleased when Ray started to show an interest in her. She rejected the pass he made at her but this only caused him to viciously insult her in a

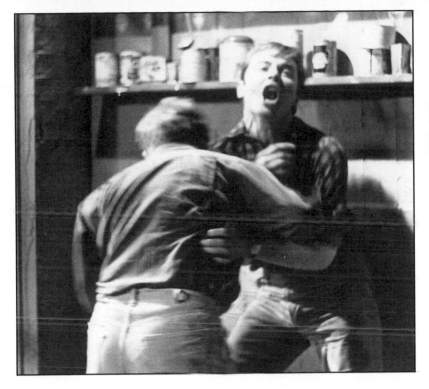

Len was furious when he heard that Ray had propositioned Elsie and had a fight with him. When he cooled down he took him in as his lodger

loud argument. When Len Fairclough found out what had happened he was furious and attacked Ray in her kitchen. Upset by the situation, Elsie threw Ray out and gave refuge for a short time to her close friend, Dot Greenhalgh who had been deserted by her husband.

Emily Nugent lived at the Rovers Return, but she fell out with her fussy landlady, Annie Walker, in late 1968, and had nowhere to go. Elsie offered her Dennis' old room which Dot

had been using and Emily gratefully accepted. Emily was a timid, virtuous soul and she resented it when Elsie used her to cover up her affair with the married Dave Smith. She didn't like Dave Smith's rude and coarse manner and thankfully escaped back to Annie Walker's safer, if stricter dwelling.

Elsie's friend, Dot, used Number 11 as a place of refuge when her husband Walter left her

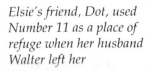

Feeling sorry for her ill sister, Elsie agreed to looking after her children, Sandra and Bernard in November 1969 (below).

Work colleague, Ivy Tilsley, (bottom) became a lodger at Number for a while but interfered too much in the Howard's marriage

Fay Butler, Elsie's widowed sister, was taken ill late in the following year and was taken into hospital for a lengthy stay. Not trusting to leave Sandra, who was obsessed with men and the accident-prone Bernard alone, she asked Elsie if she could look after her children for her. Both were trained hairdressers and Elsie employed them at Alan Howard's salon where she was working. Sandra fancied Alan but he was only interested in Elsie so she started seeing Ray Langton, Elsie's old lodger. They got engaged, but she found out he had been seeing a married woman and in disgust finished the relationship. When his mother, Fay, came out of hospital Bernard returned home to Saddleworth in Yorkshire.

Elsie married Alan Howard in the summer of 1970 and as they wanted Number 11 to themselves, Sandra was told to leave. She stayed on in the Street for a while but later left to work in London. Elsie and Alan made the most of their

time alone together before the arrival of Elsie's work colleague at the Mark Brittain warehouse, Ivy Tilsley. She had left her husband Bert on discovering him at home with a local barmaid. Bitterly upset she'd rushed round to Elsie's who felt sorry for her and let her stay the night. In the morning Ivy showed no signs of leaving and started to talk about getting a divorce. When Ivy started interfering in Elsie's marriage and got into a fight with a colleague at work who had accused her of being attracted to Alan, Elsie found she had the perfect opportunity to throw her out.

Both Alan and Elsie took pity on Lucille Hewitt when she was made homeless in 1973 and gave her a room. But when she had moved in Alan ruefully commented to his wife: 'Elsie, your heart is bigger than your head'. Lucille fell out with Alan when she supported Elsie's story that she had gone to see a friend in Sheffield, when she was really visiting Dennis in prison in Pentonville. The Howard's left Coronation Street later in the year and Lucille was forced to go back and stay with her Aunt, Annie Walker, at the Rovers Return.

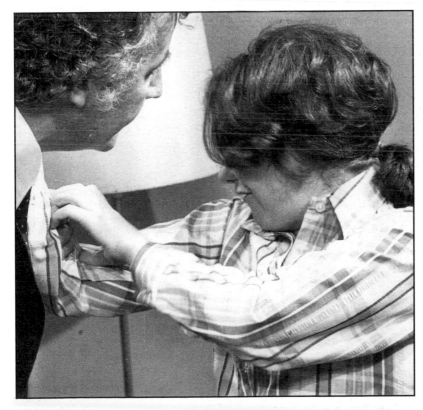

Alan turned on their young lodger, Lucille Hewitt when she wouldn't say who Elsie was visiting when she disappeared for a week

Gail Potter and Suzie Birchall

Elsie originally agreed that Suzie Birchall could stay for a week. She managed to stretch it to 18 months, sharing a room with Gail

After the break up of her marriage to Alan, Elsie returned to Coronation Street in 1976 and rented some rooms at the Corner Shop. She soon got to know Tricia Hopkins and Gail Potter who were the young girls sharing the above flat. Sometime later Elsie managed to get her house back again this time to buy it and, Gail went with her as her new lodger. When Gail moved in Elsie ruefully commented to her: 'Did I ever tell you about our Linda an' Dennis? An' the niece and nephew I 'ad stayin' with me? And I also told you 'ow livin' with kids put years on me! If they're not doin' t'wrong things, they're sayin' 'em''.

Gail was joined two months later by Suzie Birchall, a young girl who worked locally. Gail was shy and not very confident, but Suzie was the complete opposite and had a very forthright and cheeky manner. She was the ideal leader for the susceptible Gail and told Elsie horrendous tales of disreputable landlords that she had suffered, but had really heard about from Bet Lynch, to persuade Elsie to let her share Gail's room permanently.

Both the girls were obsessed with men and during their eighteen months with Elsie they tried to brighten up her life. Elsie found it hard work with two young girls under her roof; they put pressure on her men friends to propose, but worst of all, their experiences with boyfriends in growing up brought out all her maternal instincts and memories of her past love life. When Gail fell in love with her older boss, Roy Thornley, Elsie could see he was just using her, but Gail was infatuated with him and refused to listen to her advice. When Roy admitted he was married and Gail was later cited in divorce proceedings, Elsie fought for Gail's reputation and managed to convince Mrs Thornley to name another of Roy's women.

Suzie was never long without a boyfriend and when she started going out with Paul Stringer, a model agency boss in his 50s, she enjoyed the money and attention of a well-off older man. Elsie didn't approve of the relationship and sarcastically said to Paul: I'm sure we've got a lot to talk about, you and me. Like what we were both doin' on VE day. Course, that leaves Suzie out of the conversation'. Suzie was incensed when Elsie called her a tart and angrily retorted, 'Elsie Tanner you've been the biggest slut of them all!'

Trying to do Elsie a favour on her birthday in 1977 the girls attempted to clean out her chimney. All went well at first, they tied a brick to a piece of rope and lowered it down the chimney. But to their horror they had chosen the wrong chimney and Hilda Ogden walked into her parlour to find it covered in piles of soot!

Although the generation gap often showed, the two girls and Elsie had some good times and were united in their disputes with Hilda who proved to be a petty and spiteful neighbour.

Gail got married to Brian Tilsley in November 1979 and moved out of Number 11. Suzie stayed on in the house when Elsie went to live in Torquay for a while, but when she heard Elsie was thinking of selling up she pointed out patches of

Elsie tried to help Suzie in her affair with Paul Stringer (left) *and Gail with Ray Thornley* (below), *but both girls accused her of getting far too involved*

Elsie told Suzie to leave after she tried to obstruct the sale of Number 11 in December 1979

damp, cracks and encouraged Hilda Ogden to bang on the wall by playing loud music to put off prospective buyers, so she wouldn't lose her home. Elsie found out what she was doing and told her it was time to leave.

A new job working in Jim's transport café brought the odd lorry driver to Elsie's door asking for a bed for the night in 1980. Elsie fell for the charm of good-looking trucker, Dan Johnson, but soon discovered that he had women in every town he visited. He let her down even more when she discovered he was also having an affair behind her back with barmaid Bet Lynch.

Dan Johnson, Elsie's lorry driving lodger, won his way into her house with his charm and friendly manner

Martin Cheveski

Martin's romance with Karen Oldfield in the autumn of 1980 (left) upset her protective, policeman father. He told Elsie he'd threaten Martin with legal action if he continued to see her (below)

Totally disenchanted with the fickle nature of her lorry driver lodgers, Elsie happily agreed to take in Linda's second son, Martin, in the summer of 1980. Having 16 year-old Martin in the house made Elsie feel old at first but she soon appreciated his lively, young company. Len Fairclough soon offered him a job as an apprentice plumber in his building works. Martin started going out with factory girl Karen Oldfield, but he angered her policeman father when she came home drunk on Elsie's gin. Sergeant Oldfield refused to let Martin see his daughter any more, but was eventually convinced that he really loved her. When Martin proposed to Karen later in the year, she turned him down saying she was too young to marry. He felt totally rejected and returned home to Birmingham to be comforted by his parents.

Alone once more, Elsie offered a room to homeless engineer Wally Randle after he helped stop a fight at the café. Wally gratefully accepted, but never moved in when he realised she was more interested in him as a man than as a

Elsie welcomed Wally Randle into her home, but he soon got cold feet when he realised that she was attracted to him

lodger. Some months later, Gail's mother Audrey Potter stayed with Elsie for a while when she left her boyfriend. Elsie realised what she was going through as she had so often been in the same plight. She was sad to lose her friend a year later but Audrey felt it was time to move on after she had turned down a marriage proposal from Alf Roberts.

Eddie Yeats, lived next door with The Ogden's, and persuaded Elsie to rent a room to his girlfriend, Marion Willis in 1982. Elsie at first refused but she grew to like Marian's straightforward and honest character and let her move in. Life was disrupted for both of them when Suzie Birchall moved back some months later and Elsie agreed that she could share Marion's room. Marion couldn't cope with Suzie's forthright attitude and general untidiness and moved into the parlour

The household was upset by the arrival of Suzie's husband, Terry Goodwin, that nobody knew about. Suzie revealed that he used to beat her up and showed Elsie the bruises. Elsie got rid of Terry when he tried to force Suzie to return to him. Suzie then grew jealous of Gail's happy marraige to Brian and swore to Gail that he'd tried to seduce her one night when she was out. Elsie knew that Suzie had slept in her own bed that night, and supporting Gail threw Suzie out in disgust.

For once, Elsie joined forces with her enemy Hilda Ogden to keep Marion and Eddie together in their stormy

relationship. Elsie blamed herself when Eddie invested £1,000 in a car deal set up by Elsie's boyfriend, Geoff Siddall. Geoff disappeared with the money and Marion blamed Eddie for his gullible attitude and broke off their engagement. Eddie needed to get away and left the area, but to Elsie's relief, Marion went after him and tracked him down in Liverpool. After their wedding in October 1983, Eddie stayed on with Marion in the parlour at Number 11 before they both moved away to live in Bury.

Marion's turbulent romance with Eddie Yeats finally blossomed into marriage in late 1983 when she lodged at Number 11

Life at Work

'I'll sell umpteen jars of vanishing cream and daft frocks to keep meself in scampi.'

Elsie Tanner to Alan Howard

Miami Modes

Elsie was happy working at Miami Modes until Walter Fletcher (below right) offered her a better position in a proposed new shop

Elsie was often let down by her men and made several disastrous decisions in her personal life, but her working life was much more of a success. A born leader, her easy, outgoing manner was perfectly suited to the sales profession. She was a conscientious worker and people soon trusted and promoted her in most of the jobs she had. Her major character flaws, which tempered her varied career, were her poor timekeeping, and her volatile temperament. She often resigned in a fury and her sharp tongue gave her the sack from several positions.

Her first main job was working as a sales assistant in 1955 at the Slightly Better Dress Department of a Manchester store – Miami Modes. It was a store that catered for those well-off women, probably from Cheshire, who had that little bit of extra money to spend on themselves. Both Elsie and her best friend, Dorothy Greenhalgh, commonly known as 'Dot', suffered the critical tongue of their supervisor Mrs Dumbarton and had to put up with the tantrums of their misguided customers who always believed they were in the right.

Elsie was happy at the shop but was tempted to move when a representative for 'Lady Rebecca, Walter Fletcher, offered her the post of manageress in a store he was planning to open. The job offer came to

68

nothing, as did Walter, and when Mrs Dumbarton left to get married a few years later in 1963, both Elsie and and Dot applied for the vacant position. They were both shocked and disappointed when their younger work colleague, Christine Appleby, was appointed supervisor over them.

It was particularly hard for Elsie to accept as Christine had lodged with her at one time. She had also watched Christine grow up with her children Linda and Dennis, and resented her high-handed criticisms of the way Elsie dealt with customers. When Christine found Elsie using her shop discount to buy clothes for a friend, she became extremely officious and then complained about her to Personnel. A few days later Elsie took her task about the incident only to get the reply: 'I've no friends when I'm at work Elsie. Friendship stops at that door downstairs.' Elsie feared she might be sacked, but the management was aware of Christine's overpowering manner and she was then transferred.

T o help pay for the £60 that Dennis needed as his entrance fee on a hairdressing course, Elsie took an evening job a short time later at the Vaidcut Sporting Club, owned by her boyfriend, Laurie Frazer. She became a croupier and was put in charge of the roulette table. The glamorous life suited her, but she only lasted one night as one of her client's turned out to be Laurie's wife. Elsie had not known that Laurie was married and resigned in a huff, losing her lifelong membership.

Christine Appleby took Elsie to task at work in early 1963 (top). *Elsie's lucrative evening job as a croupier was doomed to failure* (bottom)

Elsie still tried to earn the extra money for Dennis by modelling in the evenings for the art students at the School of Design. She found the work quite restful, but the art teacher, David Graham, became obsessed by her and forced her to resign the job.

Life working at Miami Modes was always turbulent and after a violent row with the new supervisor, over her erratic timekeeping, Elsie resigned and walked out. Her son Dennis found the tables turned for once and, as she would have done to him, demanded that she got another job. Her experience in sales impressed Emily Nugent and she became her assistant at Gamma Garments. Working with the timid, teetotal Emily was very boring and Elsie tried to brighten her days by flirting with the more interesting male customers.

She only lasted two months and when no promotion was forthcoming she took over the job as manageress of the Laundryer, just three doors up on Rosamund Street. A few

Elsie finally left her favourite store, Miami Modes (top left) *and she then had short spells working at Gamma Garments* (top right) *and supervising washing at the Laundryer* (above)

70

Supervisor 1965

Ten years after starting work at Miami Modes, Elsie is made supervisor in late 1965 (left). Some time later she and Dot reminisced about their wartime romances when the US army returned in May 1967 (below)

months of organising other people's washing and working in the hothouse atmosphere, drove Elsie mad and when Dot suggested at Christmas in 1965 that she should return to Miami Modes she was more than willing for a change of scene. Dot was not so pleased when Elsie was appointed supervisor as she was next in line for the position.

Together with Dot, Elsie had no regrets about neglecting her work when the American GIs returned to barracks in Burtonwood a couple of years later. Before she could be sacked by the shop for her continual absences, Elsie proudly announced that she was leaving to marry Steve Tanner. After the wedding she began to get bored with nothing to do at her new home in Altrincham and was keen to start work again, but Steve made it clear her place was at home, and only a short time later her whole world was turned upside when Steve was posted back to America.

Dave Smith opened a florist shop, The Pink Posy Bowl, in the old Gamma Garments shop at 16 Rosamund Street. He took Elsie on as manageress

When Elsie left her husband in America and came back to the Street in 1968 her finances were secure as Steve had agreed to pay her alimony, but she wanted the stimulus of working with people again, so she joined Dennis' fiancée, Jenny Sutton at MacAverby's department store, helping her to demonstrate new products in the food hall. Her old flame, Dave Smith felt she was wasting her talents there and convinced her to come and work at his florist shop, 'The Pink Posy Bowl', as manageress.

As Dave and Elsie became close again, she neglected the shop, leaving her assistant Lucille Hewitt in charge. She and Dave disappeared off for days out at the local races. The romance cooled when Dave's estranged wife, Lilian sued for divorce and named Elsie as correspondent. Dave became more interested in the divorce settlement than Elsie and not long afterwards sacked her for bad timekeeping.

Dot persuaded Elsie to return to Miami Modes again, but this time it was for the last time. Elsie had not been working there for long when Dot, who was separated from her husband and staying with her at the time, took an afternoon off sick. She rang in later to ask Elsie if she would bring a bag home for her. On her way out Elsie was stopped by security who found the bag contained two dresses from the shop, which had not been paid for. Elsie was stunned and told the guard firmly she knew nothing about the dresses: 'I don't need to pinch stuff. I'm not that short of a bob or two, you can make enquiries – I only took

the rotten job on for some'at to fill me time, nothin' else. if I'd wanted them frocks I could 'ave paid for 'em ten times over and not missed it.'

Dot swore to Elsie that she had not stolen the dresses and said that there must have been a mix-up with the bags. Their stories were not believed by the store and Elsie was charged with shoplifting and the case then went to court.

On the eve of the court case Dot broke down and confessed that she had stolen the dresses blaming it on the stress of her marriage break-up. Furious with her stupidity Elsie screamed: 'How many dresses 'ave you got stacked away in the wardrobe at 'ome!' Dot begged Elsie not to say anything as she was terrified of going to jail. Elsie's convincing performance in court on oath that she knew nothing about the dresses, complete with a bandaged wrist from a recent accident, won the magistrates round and the case was dropped through lack of evidence. But Elsie and Dot were not trusted again and they were forced to resign by Miami Modes boss, Mr Maddox-Smith.

Court dispute 1969

Elsie was accused of stealing from Miami Modes (top left), which led to a court case. Dot confessed to the crime (top right) but both were asked to resign, even after Elsie's eventual acquittal, in 1969 (bottom)

The Salon

Elsie efficiently ran Alan Howard's new hairdressing salon (top) and kept her job, even though there were some changes, when it was taken over by bookie Dave Smith some three months later (bottom)

Alan Howard took over The Pink Posy Bowl in late 1969 and changed the shop into a hair salon. He took Elsie on as the new manageress and receptionist, but shortly afterwards sold out to Dave Smith. Elsie was incensed when Dave's first change was to sack Bernard Butler, who was one of the hairdresser's and also her young nephew, and led a staff walk out.

On her marriage to Alan in July 1970, Elsie gave up work as Alan convinced her that they didn't need her income. But on the return from their honeymoon she discovered it was all lies and he was on the verge of bankruptcy from his badly managed businesses. To help pay off Alan's creditors he worked as a mechanic and Elsie took a job at Charm Cosmetics, selling the products from door to door. She was so successful that within a week she was made up to area supervisor with a substantial salary increase.

Her boss, Mrs Painter, had no patience with staff who had low sales returns and asked Elsie to help sort out one of her girls, Mavis Sidlow who was not doing very well. Mavis convinced Elsie that her bad performance was because of a nervous breakdown. She aroused Elsie's sympathies who defended the girl in front of Mrs. Painter. When Elsie later ignored Mrs Painter's instructions to sack Mavis she was sacked herself before discovering that Mavis had lied to her all along and had been just been too lazy to work.

Mavis Sidlow told Elsie that her work and mental health had suffered after her husband left her (above). Elsie's boss, Mrs Painter, refused to believe Mavis' story and sacked both her and Elsie (right)

When Elsie refused Hilda a job at the warehouse (right) she told Mr Pollard about Elsie's court appearance and Elsie lost her job (above)

Luckily for Elsie she got another job straightaway demonstrating some ironmongery at Harrison and Platts. She worked long hours and became depressed trying to sell the mundane goods and never having time to go out. The opening of the Mark Brittain Mail Order Warehouse in Coronation Street seemed an golden opportunity for Elsie to change jobs and she was accepted for the position of checker supervisor. Hilda Ogden asked Elsie if she could be considered for a job in her department, but Elsie knowing Hilda wasn't up to the work refused and said: 'It's hard graft over there from 9.30 in't morning to 4.30 in't afternoon and three other women waitin' to take yer place the minute you don't deliver the goods'.

Hilda was bitterly upset when she didn't get the job and went behind Elsie's back and told the personnel manager, Mr Pollard, about her recent court appearance. Elsie lost the job and lamented to her husband, Alan: 'I can't stand another failure! I don't want another fiasco like Charmed Cosmetics –

me startin' off with a bang and coming home with me cards in me pocket'.

Pollard was replaced by Dennis Maxwell who was impressed by the way the local ladies stood up for Elsie against Hilda, and he gave her the job back. Secretly he also thought she might help him in his embezzling plans. The security of a well-paid job again was ruined when Maxwell tried to interest Elsie in his schemes to steal from the company. She refused, but didn't report him as she was scared that no one would believe her. Maxwell was later transferred to another town, much to Elsie's relief. The offer of a promotion to Birmingham, was tempting as was the salary of £1,800, but the position was working with Maxwell and Elsie was forced to turn it down. After two more years of working for Brittain's they again offered Elsie promotion in 1973, this time in Newcastle. She and Alan desperately needed a change of town, so she took the job and the Howard's moved north.

Brittain's were good employers, but Elsie found it hard to make any new friends in Newcastle and the move had not help improve her failing marriage. When she broke up with Alan she left Newcastle and returned once more to all her old friends in Weatherfield.

Dennis Maxwell was appointed personnel manager at Brittain's, and reinstated Elsie. She was put in charge of the warehouse checkers including Ivy Tilsley and Edna Gee

Sylvia's Separates

Gail and Tricia tossed a coin for a job working with Elsie (above). *Gail won and met Roy Thornley through working in the shop* (top)

Back in Coronation Street she discovered that Sylvia Matthews was looking for a sales assistant at her lingerie shop in Victoria Precinct. Elsie impressed her with her extensive sales experience and she was readily employed. The manageress was working out her notice, and by the end of her first working week Elsie was promoted to her position. Gail Potter and Tricia Hopkins, who lived in the flat above the corner shop where she was staying, both applied to be her assistant. Elsie couldn't choose between them so the girls flipped a coin and Gail got the job.

The lingerie shop put on a sale a few weeks later and Elsie managed to upset her arch enemy, Hilda Ogden, by refusing to take back a top Hilda had worn and badly scorched. To spite her, Hilda got up to her old tricks and told Sylvia one of her staff was a thief. Sylvia immediately suspected Gail and sacked her. Elsie stormed in and told her Gail was innocent before walking out herself.

Sylvia Matthews was led to suspect Gail of shoplifting and sacked her in early 1976. Elsie supported Gail and resigned on principle

When Sylvia heard the whole story she was happy to reinstate Elsie at the shop, but before long decided it was no longer profitable and closed it down. Elsie didn't want to see the shop empty and persuaded Mike Baldwin that it would make a good outlet for his factory-made denim jeans. He agreed but told her that he would be employing some young assistants to sell the jeans. Elsie was furious that he obviously thought she was too old to work in the shop, but backed down when he employed her as supervisor in his factory – Baldwin's Casuals.

In the summer of 1977 Elsie made a trip to Newcastle to see Alan to try and save their marriage. She combined the trip with trying to interest buyers in Mike's goods. She was an impressive representative and asked Mike on her return if she could be employed solely in this capacity. He flatly refused stating chauvinistically, 'It's true, buyers like t'look at a good pair o' legs while they're talkin' business. But what 'appens when the novelty wears off? That's when you need the boss man there, the man who can say yes or no there and then, and that's why, if there's any big time selling to be done – I do it!' Elsie was speechless and could only shout one word in response: 'Pig'.

Elsie's position at the factory was not an easy one, the girls treated her as management while Mike refused to confide in her as an equal. The situation became intolerable and when her taxi driver boyfriend, Ron secured her a housekeeper's job in Torquay working for a Mr Pickering, she jumped at the chance of going, but asked Mike to keep her job open for her in case she returned. She gave him a week's notice and was furious when he told her she could leave straight away, in front of all the giggling machinists. He was relieved to see her go as he was fed up with dealing with the complexities of her love life and the amount of time she had off.

Baldwin's Casuals

Elsie's supervisor job at Baldwin's found her caught between the workers (opposite, top) *and the management* (opposite, bottom). *She finally left the factory to go to a housekeeper's job in Torquay in late 1979* (below left)

Jim's Café

Jim Sedgewick employed Elsie to work in his transport cafe on Rosamund Street in February 1980

Mr Pickering didn't turn out to be a gentleman at all and was always trying to fondle Elsie. She put up with it for two months, but in late 1979 eventually couldn't stand it any more and returned home without Ron. There was not much work around and after spending three weeks searching for a job in a dress shop, Elsie accepted the position as manageress in Jim's café in Rosamund Street. She enjoyed working with the lorry drivers, they were good fun, and she was always ready with a witty retort to their basic humour. After suffering several disastrous relationships she became very depressed and stayed off work for a while, only to find on her return that she had been sacked and replaced. Desperate to earn some money, Elsie had to swallow her pride and returned to Baldwin's, not as supervisor this time, but just as a machinist.

Business started to slow down for Baldwin's Casuals and to help trade through a bad patch, Mike opened up a market stall. Elsie and Vera Duckworth were drafted in to run it. Elsie liked the cosmopolitan market atmosphere and thought about getting a stall of her own, but the cold and wet weather chilled her to the bone and convinced her it was not to be. Still trying to boost the flagging business and help Mike get a big order, Elsie went out to dinner with him and buyer Wilf Stockwell in a foursome. Wilf fell for Elsie and after a very short relationship used her as an excuse to leave his wife. Dot Stockwell was furious and went to see Wilf's moralistic boss and convinced him to cancel the order. Baldwin's were forced to go on a three-day week. The machinists blamed Elsie and wouldn't speak to

her for two months. Elsie refused to be upset by them and used their silence as a chance to insult them as much as she wanted without any chance of a comeback.

On reaching 60 Elsie decided she needed a change from her dull job as a machinist and when Ivy Tilsley resigned as supervisor, she applied to take over. Mike turned her down telling her she was too old, so she resigned with bad grace and became a barmaid at the seedy Tropicana Club. She only lasted a couple of nights working with girls a fraction of her age. The arrival of a tanned and fit Bill Gregory with tales of his life in Portugal made her realise how empty her life was. She felt there was nothing to look forward in England and left with him to pursue a better life abroad.

Alma Sedgewick sacked Elsie for being absent from work (top) *and she reluctantly returned to work at Baldwin's Casuals* (bottom)

83

Bitter Battles

'Any 'orrible lyin' bit 'o gossip that goes round if you don't know it you invent it, they don't need sewers round 'ere, they've got Ena Sharples.'

Elsie to Ena Sharples

Elsie Tanner was no stranger to enemies and battles. She was a bold, uncompromising woman who was not afraid to use her sexuality to get her own way. Most of the women round her were jealous of her glamorous appeal and the way she could so easily flirt with their susceptible husbands. Since World War 2, however, one woman in particular – a widow called Mrs Ena Sharples had become Elsie's arch enemy. She heartily disapproved of Elsie's war effort, which was basically to entertain as many American GIs as possible while her husband Arnold was away at war, and thought it her public duty to criticise Elsie at every opportunity. Years later she still couldn't forget what had gone on and was heard to comment: 'She were just the same durin' the War. Skirts up 'ere an' "got any gum chum"'.

Ena Sharples enjoyed sreading the gossip that Arnold Tanner was Elsie's latest man friend in January 1961

When Arnold Tanner returned home from the War he told Elsie he no longer cared for her and left her all alone to bring up two young children. When he suddenly reappeared sixteen years later and asked for a divorce to re-marry, Ena, saw him leaving Number 11. She couldn't resist gossiping to people in the Rovers and local shops that Elsie had taken up with a strange, new man. Elsie was incensed at people talking behind her back and placed a notice in the local paper threatening to take action on anyone slandering her name. Ena enjoyed gossiping too much to take any notice and soon made it clear to everyone that she heartily disapproved

of Elsie's affair with the dashing Naval officer, Bill Gregory, who Elsie met in October 1961.

When Bill went back to sea a few months later Elsie received an anonymous letter telling that her relationship with Bill was putting her divorce in jeopardy. Elsie immediately suspected the Rovers publican, Annie Walker, who on a recent street outing to the Blackpool illuminations had been heard to comment on Bill and Elsie, 'Have you seen our Mrs Tanner? A grandmother and behaving like a stupid schoolgirl'. Annie cleared her name by insisting that she would never lower herself to write a spiteful, anonymous letter.

Elsie then turned on the only other person she thought it could be, Ena. Their street row could be heard in all the houses and provided good entertainment for the neighbours especially when Ena at one point retorted: 'There's no smoke without a fire, an' if yer will go around flauntin' yer body ev'ry time a

Letter Dispute

Elsie warned Ena (top) *and Annie Walker* (bottom) *against slandering her name*

uniform comes in sight'. Elsie was totally humiliated when she realised that Ena would always love to talk about her but would never bother to write an anonymous letter. The mystery was solved when husband Arnold wrote apologising for his fiancée, who had viciously written the letter.

Elsie was determined to find out who wrote the letter about her relationship with Bill Gregory and accused Ena (above)

Ena and Elsie could never hope to live peacefully in the Street together for long and they had a major confrontation in January 1965. Elsie's house was suffering from a leaking roof and rising damp so she called on her landlord, Wormold, and asked him to do the repairs. He told her he was no longer the landlord and that she now had a new landlady, Ena, who had inherited the house in a will.

Determined to make the house look desperately in need of major repairs for Ena, Elsie set about making it seem

much worse. She threw water up the walls to make the wallpaper peel off, she stuffed bricks up the chimney so that smoke filled the living room and she tampered with door knobs so that they came off in Ena's hand. Ena wasn't at all impressed by the charade and was heard to comment to a friend, 'Elsie Tanner's the worse actress since Jean Harlow.'

Ena was soon faced with losing her own home as the vestry where she lived was threatened with closure by the Mission Committee, and so she gave Elsie notice to quit. Their public fight caused them both much pain. Elsie was terrified of losing the only home she'd known and screamed viciously at Ena. Both of them realised they were getting too old to fight and when it was all over Annie Walker was heard to comment, 'I think Elsie's days of screaming at street corners are over now. She's learning, as we've all had to learn at some time, how to grow old gracefully'. Elsie was relieved when Ena's home was saved and she sold the house back to her old landlord, Wormold.

Number 11 at risk

Landlord Wormold introduced Elsie to her new landlady, Ena (top left). Ena threatened to evict her in January 1965, which led to more violent confrontations (top right and bottom)

The delight of having a phone installed in December 1965 was ruined for Elsie when she was subjected to some anonymous calls a few months later. The female caller was extremely abusive to her and kept calling her a tart. Elsie laughed off the calls when they first started, but after three weeks she jumped every time the phone rang. No one knew what was wrong and it wasn't until her daughter, Linda took a call and realised what she had been going through. She wanted to call in the police, but Elsie refused as she was convinced it was someone she knew.

The unknown caller

Elsie's trendy new red lacquer phone (opposite, top) brought her anonymous, abusive phone calls. Both Len (opposite, bottom) and her daughter, Linda (left) took calls and helped to comfort Elsie

After a further call, which Linda took, Elsie popped round to see Val Barlow next door at Number 9 and found her putting the phone down. She immediately accused her of making the calls and only backed down when Val's husband, Ken, said he would sue her for slander if she didn't apologise. Close to a nervous breakdown Elsie confided in her friend Len Fairclough, 'Oh Len, it's every day. One after another...Whenever the phone rings, it's allus her...Len, I'm goin' up the wall!'

Soon everybody in the Street knew about the calls and vindictive Hilda Ogden decided to play a trick on Elsie and made an unpleasant call to her. Ena spotted her coming out of the phone box and saw that the phone book was open at the name of Tanner. She immediately told Elsie who went round and confronted Hilda. Hilda broke down and admitted making one call. Finally the real caller said she was coming round to visit Elsie. When Elsie opened the door, she was startled to find out that it was Mrs Maxwell,

Mrs Maxwell turned out to be the unknown caller. When she viciously attacked Elsie, Len found them and bravely came to Elsie's rescue

the widow of a man Elsie had met only briefly in the previous year, but who had died of a heart attack on their night out together. Moira Maxwell had always blamed Elsie for his death and had become seriously unbalanced mentally. She attacked Elsie with a knife, but luckily Len Fairclough called round as they were struggling and managed to overpower her, and she was later taken away by the police.

It was Len himself who Elsie fought against a few years later. Len had fallen in love with Janet Reid who worked in the housing department at the Town Hall in the summer of 1969. He so wanted to impress her that he spent all his money on taking her out. His earnings couldn't keep up with her expensive tastes and he went to Jack Walker asking for a loan. Jack had not got any money but told Elsie the story. She was genuinely pleased that Len had found someone, and gave Jack Walker some of the alimony from her ex-husband Steve to lend to Len so he could carry on seeing Janet. Len decided he wanted to marry Janet but she confessed to Elsie that she didn't love him.

When Janet got bored and rejected him, Len accused Elsie of jealously frightening her off and hit out at her, screaming: 'Every time you came a cropper, you turned to me. And every time you opened it all up. You turned me down alright. But would you let me go! Would you hell as like'. When Jack explained about the loan to Len he apologised to

Len's loan

Elsie was genuinely happy for Len when he fell in love with Janet Reid during the summer of 1969 (top). She wanted to help him out with money and Jack Walker acted as a go-between for her (above)

Elsie, but the humiliation of their argument still burned deep. Feeling the need to spite him, Elsie gave Ray Langton some money to set up a rival building firm. Elsie and Len were only reconciled when the success of Ray's business threatened Len's with closure.

Hilda Ogden never got on with Elsie and their petty arguments finally came to a head in February 1978. Elsie heard strange, scratching noises from the loft that were keeping her awake at night. She sent Eddie Yates, the Ogden's lodger up to investigate and he found pigeons were entering the loft space shared by Elsie and the Ogden's through a hole in the Ogden's roof. Elsie told Hilda she had a slate missing but Hilda in her spitefulness refused to repair it. Suzie Birchall, Elsie's lodger, tried to cover the hole but slipped and put her foot through Hilda's ceiling. Hilda thought Elsie had provoked Suzie to do it on purpose and retaliated by shoving her broom through Elsie's ceiling.

Len offered to repair the ceilings for £30, telling Elsie she'd only have to pay £10 of the bill. Mean as ever, Hilda refused to part with any money and war was declared. For three weeks the two parties battled. If Elsie put her washing out, Hilda used to rush out and beat her carpets. When Gail and Suzie,

Mysterious scratching noises in the loft disturbed Elsie and her young lodgers, Gail and Suzie in February 1978

Elsie's lodgers, played loud pop music on the radio, Hilda banged on the wall, and then took to turning on her radio at full volume so Elsie couldn't hear herself think. Eventually Elsie and Hilda went to a small claims court to sort out their ridiculous dispute, and the judgement was given that each party should pay for their own household repairs.

I ronically it was Hilda who saved Elsie from her toughest street battle – that of the one for her life. After a hard day serving customers at Jim's café where she worked for a time in 1980, Elsie fell asleep on her sofa and dropped her lighted cigarette onto the upholstery. A fire soon started and quickly filled the room with noxious smoke. A short time later Hilda called in through the ever open back door wanting to borrow a cup of sugar. Discovering Elsie in the living room, she rushed back to get her husband, Stan, and together they quickly dragged Elsie to safety.

Any gratitude that Elsie felt towards Hilda soon faded when she spent the next few weeks reminding Elsie, in no uncertain terms, that she had saved her life. Eventually Elsie decided that she could stand it no longer and that she'd rather have Hilda as an enemy than a friend and told her loudly to shut up, saying, 'You're the biggest gas bag since the Graf Zeppelin'.

Hilda the lifesaver

When Elsie found out that Hilda (top) *and Stan* (bottom) *had saved her from her smoke-filled living room she knew that she would be reminded of the deed for ever*

Memorable Moments

'I'm still like a little kid, me. Mekkin' sandcastles on South Shore. I only needed to see a big, blonde, feller wi "Lifeguard" plastered across 'is chest, an I'd traipse after 'im all day wi' me bucket an' spade.'

Elsie Tanner

▶ *A first kiss for Elsie and Alan in December 1969. Their tempestuous marriage lasted eight years*

▼ *The Tanner's had a last family Christmas in 1967*

▲ *The best job for Elsie was working at Brittain's from 1971–1973*

◀ *Bill's return in December 1983*

▼ *Elsie loved dressing up glamorously*

▲ *Elsie's best friend, Len, was always there when she needed him. Their minds thought alike and he always made her laugh*

The Cast

Christine Appleby	CHRISTINE HARGREAVES
Gary Bailey	WARREN CLARKE
Mike Baldwin	JOHNNY BRIGGS
Frank Barlow	FRANK PEMBERTON
Ken Barlow	WILLIAM ROACHE
Valerie Barlow	ANNE REID
Suzie Birchall	CHERYL MURRAY
Jerry Booth	GRAHAM HABERFIELD
Percy Bridges	JACK SMETHURST
Ted Brownlow	BARRIE COOKSON
Sandra Butler	PATRICIA FULLER
Bernard Butler	GORDEN KAYE
Linda Cheveski	ANNE CUNNINGHAM
Ivan Cheveski	ERNST WALDER
Paul Cheveski	MARCUS SAVILLE
Martin Cheveski	JONATHON CAPLAN
Mrs Cook	JESSE EVANS
Sheila Crossley	EILEEN MAYERS
Norah Dawson	AVRIL ANGERS
Arthur Dewhurst	ROBIN WENTWORTH
Joe Donnelli	SHANE RIMMER
Vera Duckworth	ELIZABETH DAWN
Mrs Dumbarton	DIANA COUPLAND
Len Fairclough	PETER ADAMSON
Rita Fairclough	BARBARA KNOX
Bill Fielding	JOHN JUNKIN
Walter Fletcher	DONALD MOSLEY
Gregg Flint	BILL NAGY
Laurie Frazer	STANLEY MEADOWS
Rosemary Frazer	CLAIRE OWEN
Jimmy Frazer	JOHN BARRIE
Edna Gee	MAVIS ROGERSON
Terry Goodwin	TERENCE HILLYER
David Graham	ROER ADAMSON
Dot Greenhalgh	JOAN FRANCIS
Walter Greenhalgh	DEREK BENFIELD
Bill Gregory	JACK WATSON
Phyllis Gregory	MARY QUINN
Esther Hayes	DAPHNE OXENFORD
Lucille Hewitt	JENNIFER MOSS
Tricia Hopkins	KATHY JONES
Alan Howard	ALAN BROWNING
Laura Howard	STELLA TANNER
Dan Johnson	RICHARD SHAW
'La Composita'	ANGELA DOUGLAS

Ray Langton	NEVILLE BUSWELL
Florrie Lindley	BETTY ALBERGE
Norman Lindley	GLYN OWEN
Bet Lynch	JULIE GOODYEAR
Ron Mather	JOE LYNCH
Sylvia Matthews	ROSEMARIE DUNHAM
Bob Maxwell	DONALD HEWLETT
Moira Maxwell	ANNE CASTLE
Dennis Maxwell	WILLIAM LUCAS
Jim Mount	BARRY KEEGAN
Emily Nugent	EILEEN DERBYSHIRE
Stan Ogden	BERNARD YOUENS
Hilda Ogden	JEAN ALEXANDER
Sergeant Oldfield	MICHAEL LEES
Karen Oldfield	SALLY JANE JACKSON
Mrs Painter	BARBARA MITCHELL
Harry Payne	MAX WALL
Edward Pollard	MICHAEL GOVER
Audrey Potter	SUE NICHOLLS
Gail Potter	HELEN WORTH
Walter Potts	CHRISTOPHER SANDFORD
Wally Randle	MARK EDEN
Janet Reid	JUDITH BARKER
Jim Sedgewick	MICHAEL O'HAGAN
Alma Sedgewick	AMANDA BARRIE
Ena Sharples	VIOLET CARSON
Mavis Sidlow	CARMEL CRYAN
Geoff Siddall	EDWARD JUDD
Dave Smith	REGINALD MARSH
Lillian Smith	RHODA LEWIS
Wilf Stockwell	TERENCE LONGDEN
Dot Stockwell	BARBARA YOUNG
Jed Stone	KENNETH COPE
Monica Sutton	ANGELA PLEASENCE
Paul Stringer	JOHN COLLIN
Elsie Tanner	PATRICIA PHOENIX
Arnold Tanner	FRANK CRAWSHAW
Wally Tanner	GEORGE BETTON
Steve Tanner	PAUL MAXWELL
Dennis Tanner	PHILIP LOWRIE
Jenny Tanner	MITZI ROGERS
Roy Thornley	SIDNEY LIVINGSTONE
Brian Tilsley	CHRISTOPHER QUINTEN
Ivy Tilsley	LYNNE PERRIE
Annie Walker	DORIS SPEED
Jack Walker	ARTHUR LESLIE
Ted Wormold	IVOR DEAN
Eddie Yeats	GEOFFREY HUGHES
Marion Yeats	VERONICA DORAN